THIS WALKER BOOK BELONGS TO:

_____

_____

_____

_____

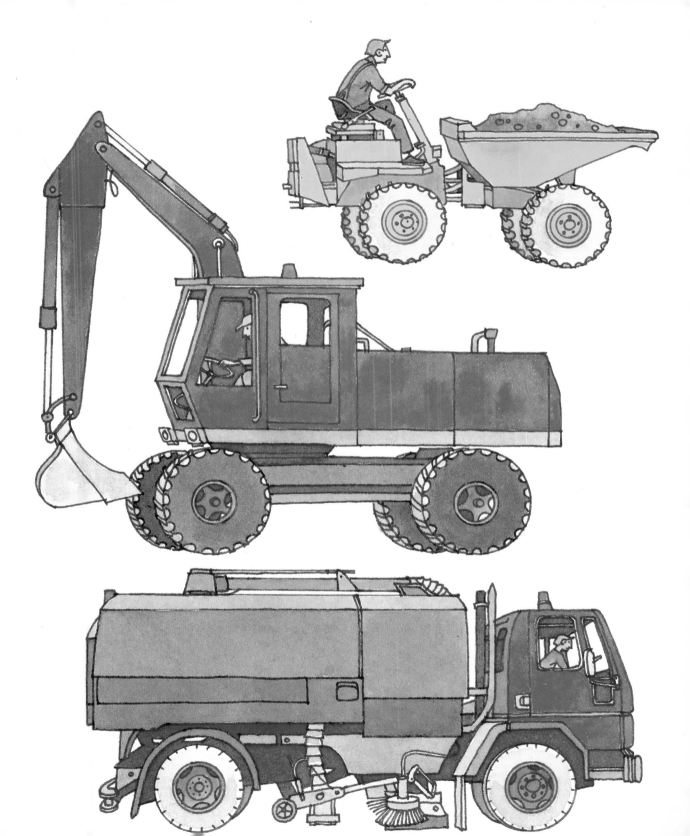

For Simon

First published 1988 by
Walker Books Ltd
87 Vauxhall Walk
London SE11 5HJ

© 1988 Gaynor Chapman

First printed 1988
Printed in Spain by Cayfosa

British Library Cataloguing in Publication Data
Chapman, Gaynor
Road works. — (Machines at work).
1. Road construction — Juvenile literature
2. Roads — Maintenance and repair —
Juvenile literature
I. Title   II. Series
625.7′94   TE149

ISBN 0-7445-0916-5

Machines
at Work

ROAD WORKS

Gaynor Chapman

WALKER BOOKS
LONDON

Drainpipes are going to be laid.

First the workers use drills
to break up the road.

A lorry brings the drainpipes to the
site and stacks them by the roadside.

9

A backhoe loader, with a digger on
one end and a scoop on the other,
digs a trench.

An excavator pushes metal sheets
down the sides of the trench
to stop the earth from falling in.

The backhoe digs out the earth.

Then it tips it into a truck
which will take it away.

A water-pump pumps away the water.

The excavator gently lowers the pipes
into the trench to be fitted together
one at a time.

Then the backhoe-scoop pushes earth
and sand over the pipes.

The concrete mixer arrives with concrete to finish the manhole.

23

A tractor leaves a pile of tar and stones for the workers to rake evenly over the unmade road.

A roller smooths over the new patch
of road while it is still soft.

Finally the road sweeper cleans the road.

Now cars can drive on it again.

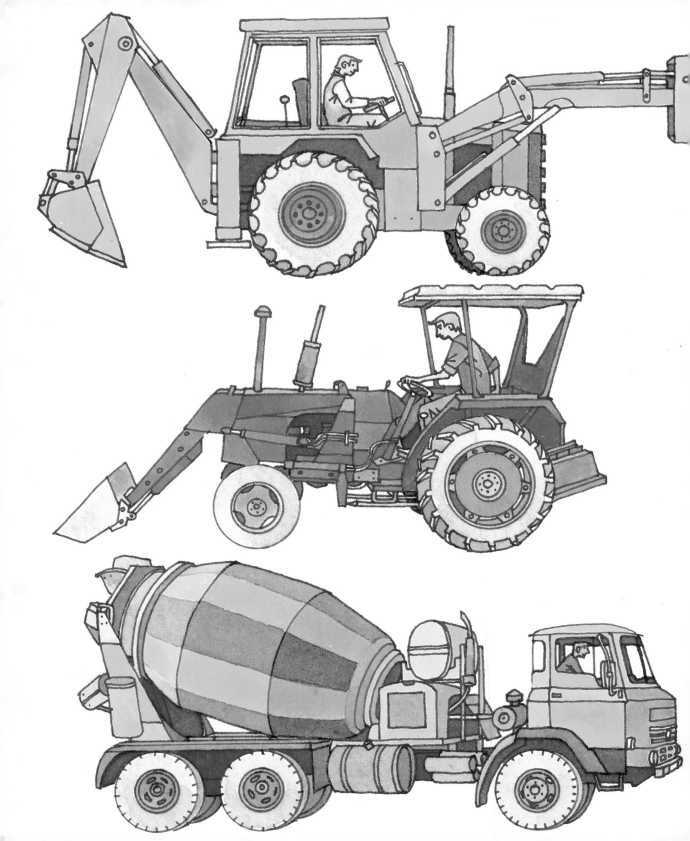

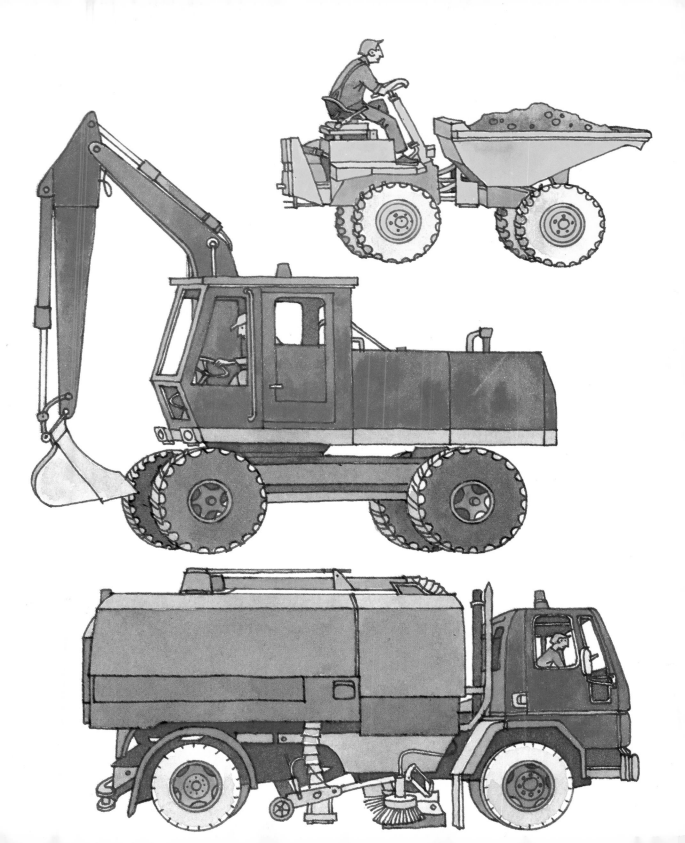

MORE WALKER PAPERBACKS

BABIES' FIRST BOOKS

Jan Ormerod
Dad and Me
READING   SLEEPING
DAD'S BACK   MESSY BABY

Marie Wabbes
Little Rabbit
LITTLE RABBIT'S GARDEN
LITTLE RABBIT'S BIRTHDAY
IT'S SNOWING, LITTLE RABBIT
GOOD NIGHT, LITTLE RABBIT

LEARNING FOR FUN
The Pre-School Years

Shirley Hughes
Nursery Collection
NOISY
COLOURS
BATHWATER'S HOT
ALL SHAPES AND SIZES
TWO SHOES, NEW SHOES
WHEN WE WENT TO THE PARK

Philippe Dupasquier
Busy Places
THE GARAGE   THE AIRPORT
THE BUILDING SITE
THE FACTORY   THE HARBOUR
THE RAILWAY STATION

Tony Wells   Puzzle Books
PUZZLE DOUBLES
ALLSORTS

John Satchwell & Katy Sleight
Monster Maths
COUNTING   SHAPES
ODD ONE OUT   BIG AND LITTLE

PICTURE BOOKS
For The Very Young

Helen Oxenbury
Pippo
No. 1 TOM & PIPPO READ A STORY
No. 2 TOM & PIPPO MAKE A MESS
No. 3 TOM & PIPPO GO FOR A WALK
No. 4 TOM & PIPPO AND THE
    WASHING MACHINE
No. 5 TOM & PIPPO GO SHOPPING
No. 6 TOM & PIPPO'S DAY
No. 7 TOM & PIPPO IN THE GARDEN
No. 8 TOM & PIPPO SEE THE MOON

Helen Oxenbury
First Picture Books
PLAYSCHOOL   EATING OUT
THE DRIVE   OUR DOG
THE CHECK-UP   THE VISITOR
THE BIRTHDAY PARTY
GRAN AND GRANDPA
THE DANCING CLASS